Ka The Indian Boy

and

David Brainerd, The Indian's Missionary

Grace & Truth Books
Sand Springs, Oklahoma

ISBN # 1-58339-134-7

First printings, 1700's (date unknown)
Printed by Triangle Press, 1996
Current printing, Grace & Truth Books, 2002

Cover design by Ben Gundersen

Grace & Truth Books
3406 Summit Boulevard
Sand Springs, Oklahoma   74063
Phone: 918 245 1500

www.graceandtruthbooks.com
email: gtbooksorders@cs.com

TABLE OF CONTENTS

Oh! send God's holy Book where'er
The winds can waft, or waters bear;
Let India's Sons its page revere,
Let Afric's land the blessing share.

Send it to where, expanded wide,
The South Sea rolls its farthest tide;
To every island's distant shore
Make known the Saviour's grace and power.

Send it to every dungeon's gloom,
Send it to every poor man's room;
Nor cease the woe-worn to befriend,
Nor cease the heavenly gift to send.

May every seeking child of woe
Its truths believe, its comforts know;
May every hand the treasure hold,
And error's cloud away be roll'd.

The Holy Ghost, who gave the word,
Must with His truth the light afford,
Bestow His quickening, saving power.
On all the soul His blessing shower.

His grace can turn the wanderer's eye
To Him who did for sinners die,
And sin and sorrow hence be driven,
And earth be chang'd from earth to heaven

CHAPTER ONE

The Battle and the Escape

"The Indian hut, the English cot,
Alike God's care must own;
Though savage nations know Him not,
But worship wood and stone."

It is well known that not infrequently the most desperate conflicts have taken place between different tribes in North America. It was early on a summer's morning, when two tribes met on the banks of a river, that a battle commenced between the parties, which terminated in the defeat and almost the destruction of one tribe. The prisoners were reserved for a cruel death; and among these unhappy people was the wife of a chief, with her little son, a child who apparently had not reached the age of seven years. She lay at a little distance from the spot on which the battle had been fought, and which was now strewed with the dead bodies of her late associates, lamenting her hard fate. The tears rolled down her cheeks as she looked at her little boy, whom she had fondly hoped would one day be praised by his tribe for his valour; but now all was lost. Her husband, whom she had sincerely loved, and by whom likewise she had been tenderly loved, was amongst the slain, and she hoped therefore that the enemy would deprive her of life. Yet again, when she cast her eyes upon her child, she wished to live, for his sake. She considered that she might escape, and began to look on every side for that purpose; but no opportunity occurred: all eyes were upon her, and upon the other unfortunates. She saw them slain one after another, and beheld the little ones led away; and now she expected herself to be dispatched, and to be torn forever from her only child: yet no one approached her with any hostile intention. She was indeed rather of a dark complexion, with graceful features and fine flowing

1

hair, and was considered beautiful. This was, perhaps, the reason her life was spared.

At length, she saw no one looking toward the place where she sat; her enemies were busily engaged in examining the valuables which were scattered about the ground for some distance. She seized the opportunity, put her fingers upon the lips of the child, thus indicating the necessity of silence (which sign the child had been taught to understand), and then she bade him carefully follow her. She silently crept along the ground; the boy did the same. In a few minutes they got among the bushes, and were not long before they entered a wood. She arose, and then taking the child by the hand, said, "Kanousky, we must run!" Neither she nor the child had been unaccustomed to this exercise. They quickened their pace till they were a considerable distance from their enemies; and they would have proceeded farther, but fatigue compelled them to stop and take rest. Whether the enemies pursued we know not, for she saw them no more.

Sazia (for that was her name) was so overcome with bodily exertion, and by the distress which her mind had sustained, that she sank into a deep sleep: her boy was not long before slumber closed his eyes, and they both slept till the next morning's sun darted its friendly beams upon them. She awoke some time before her child. At first, when looking around, she seemed lost in astonishment; sleep had for a little while removed from her that weight of trouble which the day before had almost overwhelmed her. But too soon did the Indian widow call to mind the sad events of yesterday. She was lost in thought, but involuntarily turning her head, she saw her boy sleeping near her side; then the big tears rushed from her eyes and rolled down her cheeks. She seemed deprived of all comfort. The transactions of the day before, which had been so numerous, and which crowded upon her, left then but little time for reflection; but now too her mind, that had been refreshed with sleep, felt her sad lot more than when it was worn by a succession of events. She wept, and wept much; great was her trouble, and she had no comforter: she knew not God; how therefore could she pray to Him?

CHAPTER TWO

A New Home Discovered

When Kanousky awoke, she pressed him to her bosom, and with him walked away; but whither she was going she knew not, and as she journeyed, she wept and sobbed deeply.

"My mother," said the little Indian, "why do you cry?"

"All our people are dead, my child; your father is dead, and you and I are wandering about in a forest of which we know nothing, and I have no food for you."

"Do not cry, my mother, or else I must cry. When I am a man I will avenge the injuries of my own nation."

Such a speech will not excite surprise, when it is known that one of the leading characteristics of the Indian is revenge, and that it is taught as a duty to the children of Indians as soon as they begin to reflect.

"May it be so, my boy," replied Sazia. They continued travelling in an uncertain direction, until one day when, the mother and child having been in search of some food, such as roots, and whatever they could find upon which they could exist, they were unfortunately separated. The boy saw some wild fowl which he vainly pursued, hoping to take; and it was not till after some time that finding his chase was useless, he thought of returning to his mother, but he could not retrace his steps. He wandered about till night, and the next morning he attempted to find the place at which he had left his mother, but all his efforts were again useless. His grief we can imagine better than describe, and we may in some degree conceive the depths of that anguish with which the heart of the Indian widow was afflicted. Kanousky sat down for a long time, not knowing what step to take. At length he ran from place to place, crying out as loud as possible for his mother; but he cried in vain. In the most disconsolate state he wandered about the woods for many days, living upon roots and wild fruits when he could meet with any, until one morning he found himself in an open country, and saw at a distance some men. He was overjoyed at this sight, and ran towards them, hoping that they might be able to give some account of his mother. But as he drew near to them, he saw that they were a different kind of persons from those whom he had been accustomed to see; their dress was new to him, and they carried what he supposed to be weapons, but which were working tools, such as he never before had seen. He stopped; he was afraid of advancing; he was also fearful of returning to the woods, which had been to him, since he lost his mother, most dreary and solitary.

While he was debating in his mind what to do, one of the party made signs to him to approach. Kanousky went forward timidly, but yet drew nearer to the men, who did all they could by smiles and signs to show that their intentions were most friendly. The men were the servants of a rich farmer who resided in that neighbourhood. They spoke to Kanousky, and Kanousky to them, but all that was said was not known to either party. The little boy in his own language made repeated inquiries for his mother; yet, though they saw that he was in distress, no one could make out what the boy wanted. They had some refreshment with them, part of which they gave him. The child, having this testimony of their kindness, dried up his tears and embraced them one after the other. They were all pleased with him, and, not without his consent, they took him to their master's house. Their master gave him a kind reception.

Kanousky was clothed, and lodged in the farmer's house; and he amused himself in the day-time with some of the labourer's children. They pointed out various things to him, and taught him to call them by their proper names, so that in a very little time he was able to understand many things that were said to him, and to answer almost every question that was put to him. When he could converse pretty tolerably with his new associates, his master thought it was proper to give him some light, easy employment, so he was sent out with other lads to weed in the field. He daily increased in the goodwill of his master and of all the servants. After work he used to be very entertaining to his fellow-servants (for we must now consider him in the character of a servant), by exhibiting the various games common among his native tribe.

Thus he continued to be the favourite of all about him, and seemed to be as happy as any of them, except when he thought of his mother, the remembrance of whom frequently came across his mind; and then he was exceedingly depressed and sad.

But, alas for Kanousky! he lived among people who seemed to be as ignorant of God as the tribe from which he himself had sprung. They called themselves Christians, but really knew nothing of Christianity. There was not a place of worship of any description within fifty miles, and Sunday was known to them only as a day of pastime and pleasure. The farmer had only the fragment of a New Testament in his house. His desires were limited to this world. He was a very kind and amiable man, but knew nothing of the power of godliness. His servants cared as little about another world as he did; in short, they never seriously thought about God, or heaven, or hell. If they did, they never uttered their thoughts on such subjects; and when the name of the blessed God was used, it was only in a profane manner.

CHAPTER THREE

A Visit to the Town

"How shall they believe in Him
of whom they have not heard?
and how shall they hear without a preacher?"
—Romans 10:14

It happened that once a year a servant by the name of Joseph went to the nearest town, which was about fifty miles distant from his master's house. He had on one occasion when he went there, amused his friends with an account of Kanousky's being found at the side of the wood, of his games and tricks, and of any other things about him which were of an interesting kind. The last time he was at the town they begged him when he came again to bring Kanousky, with which request he promised to comply, if his master would not oppose it. His master gave him permission to take the Indian, and Kanousky, who was not without that spirit of adventure so common to the tribes in America, caught at the proposal and went. He was well received by Joseph's friends.

How wonderful are the ways of God! and how often do apparently trifling circumstances lead to the calling in of His ransomed sheep! The visit of Kanousky to the town seemed to be only an ordinary occurrence, but from this journey resulted a most important affair. While he was there—for he remained in that place about a fortnight—he used sometimes to loiter about the town by himself, gazing at every object with wonder and delight; everything he saw was quite new to him. He would sometimes amuse himself at the window of a tailor's shop; then at a cutler's; then at a watchmaker's; and so on.

One morning, when he was straying out as usual, he found the shops closed, and the people that he met differently dressed. He knew not what to make of this; then as he

7

walked forward he heard a noise. He listened to ascertain from what quarter it came, and, discovering it, he proceeded towards it. Presently he came to a large building. Here he stopped, and seeing a man about to enter it, he said, "Massa, what for they make that noise in that large house?" The stranger eyed Kanousky for a moment, being surprised at the nature of the question, and wondering who the lad might he that he should thus interrogate him. He thought that it might be only Kanousky's impertinence that dictated such a question to him, and that the imperfect manner in which he spoke might be assumed. But before he replied, Kanousky, who had sufficient penetration to perceive that the man was thinking whether or not to answer him, added, "Me no impudent, massa; me Indian; me come here far away with friend." His simple manner convinced the man that he spoke the truth. The stranger replied, "They are praising God in that house."

"Praising God, what is that?"

"Come in and see," replied the man. Kanousky followed him into the chapel, and sat down beside him. After the psalm had been sung, and the other part of the service gone through, the minister commenced his sermon from this verse: "We must all appear before the judgment-seat of Christ, that every one may receive the things done in his body, according to that he hath done, whether it be good or evil." In the sermon the minister said much about the awfulness of the day of judgment to wicked people; as Christ would judge men for their thoughts, words, and works.

Kanousky was very attentive during the whole of the sermon. He found everything the preacher said to be new to him. He felt uneasy as he returned home, thinking that if there were such a place as hell, and such a day to come as the day of judgment, when the wicked would be sent to that dreadful place of misery and despair, his sad lot would be among those who would be punished. He tried, however, to forget what he had heard, but in vain, for it was no light subject on which the preacher had discoursed, and parts of his

8

sermon were at present too deeply engraven upon his mind. These were his reflections: "The gentleman tell me I must die: that me know. He say me be sinner, and that God will judge me and punish me. Me never hear before me be sinner; me never hear of God or hell. Me will tell Joseph, he set me right."

As soon as he saw Joseph, he said to him, "Well, Joseph, me met with a strange thing."

"What's the matter now?" replied Joseph: "you look, indeed, as though you had met with a strange thing."

"When me leave you," answered the Indian, "me go here and there, through one street or another, till me hear loud noise; so me try and find out where this noise come from; me do find out, and it come from large house. Me see one man, and ask what the noise mean; he ask me to go in. When me go in, me see a gentleman on high place, and he talk very much; and he speak about God, and Christ, and death, and judgment, and hell. He frighten me very much. If what he say be true, you and me and our servants be very bad, and we all go to place of punishment when we die."

"Oh," said Joseph, "make yourself happy, you need not mind what he says."

"But he make me unhappy; he talk about the great God, that great God will judge bad people, and send them to hell."

"Don't tease yourself about these things, Kanousky; you'll do better without them. Why, boy, have you not been happy without knowing anything about them?"

"Yes," replied Kanousky.

"Well, then, continue to live as you have, and think no more about them, and you'll be as happy as you were."

"Me like be happy, Joseph; but if there be such a place, me no like to go to hell when me die; gentleman say, hell be miserable place."

"Pooh!" answered Joseph, "you won't go to hell, boy."

"But is there such a place?" inquired Kanousky, eagerly.

"Yes," said Joseph, with some hesitation.

"What be such place for? Who live there?" asked the Indian.

"Thieves and murderers go there when they die," said Joseph.

"Me like know more about this. But gentleman talk much about God. Me think me hear that name before," said Kanousky. "Yes, me hear you cry out that name sometimes, and the other servants sometimes do the same. You and they often say God when angry, but then me think nothing of it."

The simplicity of this speech made Joseph laugh, but the lad's observations ought to have excited a different disposition of mind in Joseph. Kanousky, however, waited for an answer: presently Joseph replied, "God made you and all the world."

"God made me and all the world!" exclaimed Kanousky, "me never hear that before. Me like know more about this thing."

"Well," muttered Joseph, "say no more about it now, or we must think of setting out home."

CHAPTER FOUR

Conscience Silenced
and Conviction Renewed

"Shall men pretend to pleasure,
Who never knew the Lord?
Can all the worldling's treasure
True peace of mind afford?"

On their journey home, as they rode along, Kanousky asked many questions about what they had been previously conversing; but the subject was not interesting to Joseph, and he therefore avoided it as much as possible, and talked upon other matters.

In the evening Kanousky retired to rest, but he could not sleep. He still had depicted before his mind the horrors of the bottomless pit. When he reflected upon his past life, he thought himself wicked, very wicked; he was afraid to go to sleep, lest he might die and awake in hell. The night following his rest was disturbed by similar reflections.

It was soon evident to every one that something more than ordinary was the matter with him. He lost his wonted cheerfulness, and when he attempted to be as merry as formerly; every one saw that his mirth was but assumed. His master perceived the change, and, having a great regard for his Indian servant, asked him if he were well?

"Yes, me very well; me very well, massa, me thank you," replied the lad.

"But you do not appear happy, my boy."

"Me be not so happy as me was, massa."

"Why not, Kanousky?"

"Me been thinking about God and hell."

"How came you to think about these subjects?"

Kanousky here informed his master what we have before stated to our readers respecting his going into the chapel, and what he heard there.

"Is that all that renders you uncomfortable?" said his master.

"Yes, it makes me very sad."

"Well, then, don't be unhappy any longer."

"Me don't want to go to hell, massa."

"You need not be fearful of that place."

"Yes, massa, but gentleman say me be sinner, and that all sinners go there."

"You are no sinner, Kanousky; only thieves and murderers, and such persons, are sinners. You are a good servant, and do your duty. I wish all the world were as good as you. Go to your work, and be merry as a lark, boy."

"Thank you, massa; me try to be happy."

Kanousky began his usual work. His fellow-servants were determined to laugh him out of his religion. As soon as he had joined them, they inquired of him whether he had got rid of his gloomy notions? He replied that he should try to think of them no longer, and that he hoped to be as merry as formerly.

From this period Kanousky endeavored to stifle every conviction, and to forget all those subjects which had excited alarm in him. Indeed, he appeared to every one to become more than usually merry.

But when God begins His work, He will not allow convictions to be finally stifled. This mercy was displayed towards Kanousky. After he had pursued his sinful career for a time, unchecked by conscience, the words "hell" and "judgment" would rush into his mind and fill him with terror; and the idea of death would become more and more dreadful. He often said to himself, "All the people say there is a God, me know me must die, me know me a sinner. Me be told, me believe there is a hell; then me more miserable, for me know when me die me unhappy."

Before his companions he appeared cheerful. However, he did not now dare to propose any sinful pleasure. Inwardly he was torn with remorse for the past, and with dreadful apprehensions of the future. When he found himself alone he would frequently utter these words: "O me, unhappy Kanousky! me know me be sinner, great sinner; O miserable me! What shall me do? Massa say me no sinner, and yet me feel me sinner. Yet why should me be unhappy? But me have something in my heart, me cannot be quiet, and that tell me be miserable, that me must be unhappy when me die."

Often, when he poured forth these expressions of his tortured heart, he would cast himself upon the ground in an agony of tears, and almost sink into despair. How pitiable was the state of this poor youth—he had heard that which made him miserable; he had, as yet, no comforter. He dared not apply to those around him for counsel, for they derided him, whenever he entered upon the solemn subjects of death and judgment. To please them he had attempted to stifle conviction; but he could succeed only for a time, and now the flame within him burst forth with greater heat. Sleep but seldom visited his eyes; he became almost a stranger to the quiet it affords except when exhausted nature sank itself into slumber.

As he lay sleepless one night, he for the first time remembered, that the minister whom he had heard preach told his hearers to seek mercy from God. Kanousky remembered, too, that the minister spoke to God, though God did not seem present; he felt encouraged from these recollections to pray for mercy, and accordingly, the greater part of the night he kept fervently supplicating. "God, have mercy upon me; I do not see You, but You see and hear me: God, have mercy upon me." When he arose he felt comforted. Throughout the day, when alone, he still prayed, "God, have mercy upon me."

This was the substance of his prayer for many months, and he always felt his mind calmed, and in a measure comforted, whenever he used these words. His fellow-servants saw there was a change in him, for he avoided everything that was wrong; but, however, they did not know the motive from which he acted, and therefore he did not incur their laughter.

CHAPTER FIVE

The Bible Purchased

"Thy Word is a lamp unto my feet,
and a light unto my path."
—Psalm 119:105

A whole year had now passed away since Joseph had been to town, and he was about to go there again. When the time arrived, Kanousky expressed a wish to be permitted to accompany Joseph, for he thought he should hear more about the solemn subject which had so much engaged his attention for the last twelve months. His request was granted, and with a most joyful, though trembling heart, he mounted the horse which was to convey him to the town.

On Sunday, he, according to his intentions, went to the chapel into which he had formerly wandered. Here his mind was agitated between hope and fear alternately. One moment he hoped he should hear and know more about God, and then he was afraid lest that knowledge might make his state of mind worse than it had already been. Presently he saw the same gentleman who had said so much to alarm him last year. When the minister prayed, one part of the prayer very much struck Kanousky. It was this, "That God would in His mercy bring some wandering sinner into that place; and that those who were troubled in their minds might receive that heavenly peace which none can take away." When the Indian heard these words, he exclaimed, loud enough to be heard by many persons, "That me! Me wandering sinner, me want comfort!" Those who heard him speak these words aloud looked upon him and soon perceived, by his dress, that he was a stranger, though they did not say anything to him, as he seemed not to have intended to disturb the service but really to feel what he had expressed.

At length the minister commenced his sermon from these words, "Him that cometh to Me I will in no wise cast out." In the course of the sermon, he spoke much of God's goodness in sending His Son to be the Saviour of sinners; and said that, however wicked people had been, if they obeyed Christ's invitation, God would have mercy upon them. Kanousky heard all this with delight; and when at last the congregation dispersed, he eagerly inquired when the minister would preach again? Somebody told him there was to be another service that day in the chapel. He did not fail to attend.

In the course of the day he understood sufficiently to be confirmed that he was what he had felt himself to be – a sinner; and that God's Son, Jesus Christ, was a Saviour, and that God's mercy was to be sought through Jesus Christ.

Kanousky remained in the town for a month, as Joseph had much business to transact; in this he found Kanousky very useful to him. During the whole time Kanousky went regularly to the chapel twice every Sunday. He wished very much to speak to the minister before he left the town, but he was afraid; nor did he know any one to whom he could communicate what had taken place in his mind. However, during his residence in the town, he had become much attached to the children of the house in which he and Joseph took up their abode; and they, being also very fond of him, had succeeded in teaching him to read the letters of the alphabet, and some easy words.

Before he went away he was determined to buy a book, and for that purpose went to a shop and asked for one. The shopkeeper very naturally asked him what book he would have. He replied, he wished for a book such as the gentleman at the chapel read out of. Accordingly the man, who was a religious character, sold him a Bible, and then made him a present of some little easy tracts. Kanousky went out of the shop very happy, thanking the proprietor; and it was not long before he was on his way home.

16

Kanousky, The Indian Boy

After Kanousky's arrival at his master's house, he took every opportunity of improving himself in reading; and in no very long time he could read, without much difficulty, a chapter in the New Testament and also the tracts which the bookseller had kindly given him. He read with an anxious desire to obtain all the knowledge he could from his little library; and as he was in earnest, God blessed his diligence, so that every month he grew in knowledge.

By comparing himself with the description given by our blessed Lord, he found that his heart was full of sin, that it was also "deceitful above all things, and desperately wicked." At the same time he experienced within himself that truth, "Without Me ye can do nothing;" and found, that it is only by the assistance of God's Spirit we can overcome sin. He read, and believed also, that this aid is granted to them only who have repentance towards God, and faith in our Lord Jesus Christ;" and that promise of the Saviour encouraged him, "Ask, and it shall be given you; seek, and ye shall find; knock, and it shall be opened unto you."

Kanousky had learned to pray, feeling his need; and many an evening, after he had concluded his work, would he retire into the midst of a large clump of fir-trees with his Bible and tracts. There he would read, and after having read, he would on his bended knees offer up prayer, praise, and thanksgiving.

His retirement could not but be noticed by his fellow-servants; and they would have derided him for it, but his master, who found Kanousky now the best servant he had, would not allow them to molest him, observing that as long as he did not force his religion upon them, they had no right to interfere with him.

It was on a beautiful summer's evening, when Kanousky had withdrawn himself to his favorite clump of firs, that he read the account of the sufferings and death of the Lord Jesus Christ. Unknown to him, there was a man (who was one of his master's household, and who wandering that way, amused himself by smoking a pipe), overheard him thus talking to himself, and to his God and Saviour:

"Ah, Kanousky," said the poor boy in his soliloquy, "you are a great sinner. O! that that dear Saviour should suffer so much! Heart, why do you not feel more sorrow for your wickedness? Break, strong heart; weep rivers of tears. O blessed God, soften my hard heart! My heart grieve, O blessed Saviour, but not enough for my sins. Make me more grieve. Create in me a new heart, O God, and renew a right spirit within me. O! me love you, my Saviour; when me can kiss your wounded hands and feet? But no, Kanousky only Indian boy, that too much honour for Kanousky; but me must, me like to love you. You know me love you, you see my heart. O! me thank you for bringing me to the town; me praise you for leading me to chapel: me glad me suffer once pain in me heart, else me no feel joy in my heart now, nor hope to go to heaven when me die. But oh! my dear God and Saviour, remember my massa, and also Joseph, who took me to the town; and remember my fellow-servants; make them happy; make them love you, then they will be happy. Make me good servant; make me all good. Me deserve no mercy, me deserve punishment; me great sinner, but dear Saviour say to sinners, 'Him that cometh unto Me I will in no wise cast out.' Me come to Him for His goodness and love; me ask for all these blessings."

While he thus meditated and prayed, tears and smiles, by turns, were on his face. Before he left this spot, he offered up a prayer on behalf of his mother, if she were yet living. The man was struck with astonishment at what he heard and crept away silently; from that time he felt a respect for Kanousky, and if ever he needed an advocate, espoused his cause.

CHAPTER SIX

The Persecution Comes

"Blessed are they which are persecuted for righteousness'
sake; for theirs is the kingdom of heaven."
—Matthew 5:10

For a long time Kanousky had heard, with much pain,
the profane language of those around him, though he had
never yet ventured to remonstrate with anyone; but he had
often thought it his duty not to hear the name of God taken in
vain without saying something. At last he resolved to speak,
and accordingly, one day, when much swearing was going
on, he said, "O, do not swear so; God is my dear, my best
Friend, we should reverence His Name." This he uttered with
great kindness and mildness of manner: yet the scoffers
derided him, and from that day a system of persecution
commenced, which he bore with exemplary patience; but he
had now indeed learned, when he was reviled, not to revile
again! And thus when they jeered and jested, he prayed for
them, and frequently would in a whisper repeat the words of
his Saviour, "Father forgive them, they know not what they
do."

The man who had been the listener at the side of the
clump of firs would sometimes say a little on Kanousky's
behalf; but as they laughed at his interference and asked him
if he were going to be a saint too, he was soon frightened and
became silent. Yet he always acted kindly to Kanousky, and
his kindness increased to the Indian lad in proportion as their
hatred became more rooted. The servants could allege
nothing against Kanousky, but his deeds and words were such
as condemned theirs; and as the ancient scribes and Pharisees
hated the Saviour because their darkness would not endure
His light, so they disliked Kanousky.

Kanousky, The Indian Boy

The people of the world love those who are like them. Our Indian was not of the world, but had become a citizen of the New Jerusalem. The master saw that something was amiss, and was sorry; for though he knew nothing about religion, he loved peace. He interfered, and as Kanousky seemed to be the weaker party, took up for him. This produced ill-will against him, as well as against Kanousky; and the malcontents at last declared that either Kanousky should leave the house or that they would seek work elsewhere. The master, who cared and thought about his worldly affairs too much to act justly in such a case, told Kanousky he must part with him, and that this happened in consequence of the resolution which all his servants had taken. He tried, however, with good words to console the lad; and having given him some money, in a few days our young Indian departed from his service. The man who at times had been his friend also took a kind leave of him.

Before he left, Kanousky, in the presence of his master, besought God to bless him and all his household; and he declared that he left them all in peace and love, and hoped that they would part with him in the same spirit. In token of his good-will, he shook each of them by the hand. The servants were surprised and ashamed at witnessing his conduct; and some of them were even sorry when they saw Kanousky walk away with his bundle of clothes. But their pride was too great to permit them to express their feelings, and they and Kanousky now parted, perhaps never to meet again in this world.

As the youth (for he was now seventeen years of age) walked away, he felt troubled; and when he had reached some little distance from the house, he turned about to look at it for the last time. When he saw it, the tears rushed into his eyes, and plentifully ran down his face; and he exclaimed, "Ah, poor Kanousky! a few years ago thou lost thy dear mother, and now thou hast lost all thy friends." Tears prevented utterance for a few moments: when he could speak, he resumed, "No, Kanousky, thou hast not lost all thy friends;

20

thou hast thy best Friend Jesus; dear Saviour, He is always by thee; and, O! thou hast got thy Bible." As he said this, he drew it out of his pocket and kissed it; and then put it to his heart, and pressed it, adding, "Better to me than all the world. Well, God bless my massa, Joseph, and all the servants; they have been more kind to me than unkind." See the spirit and temper of this lad: he thought more upon the kindness than upon the ill-will which he had received.

Kanousky walked on, not doubting but that God would take care of him. He had walked a considerable distance on the road towards the town, determining to seek for employment there. Night was now drawing on, and he began to look for a place of rest. He saw, at the distance of half a mile, some trees; he made for this spot, and here he resolved to take up his night's repose. When he arrived, he read that portion of Scripture in which an account is given of Jacob's journey from his father's house; and of his having the earth for his bed, and a stone for his pillow.

To Kanousky it was no great inconvenience to sleep in the open air, as he had frequently done so before, and generally did when a child. "Well," said the solitary lad, as he read, "God take care of Jacob, God will take care of me, so me lay myself down." He took out from a little bag some provision, and having eaten it, he knelt down and thanked God for all His mercies, and prayed for the forgiveness of all his sins. After this he committed himself to the Divine keeping. He then laid himself down and soon fell into a sweet sleep, from which he did not awake till the singing of the birds above him announced that the sun had commenced its daily work of praise to its great Creator.

When he arose, he blessed God for protecting him and besought Him to be with him through the day, to direct him, and to lead him to some Christian person in the town to which he was going. He now walked forward, and, as he proceeded, ate his bread with thankfulness, not doubting but that he should succeed in obtaining work.

CHAPTER SEVEN

His Employment and Baptism

"Whatsoever thy hand findeth to do, do it with
thy might; for there is no work, nor device,
nor knowledge, nor wisdom, in the grave,
whither thou goest."
—Ecclesiastes 9:10

It was when the sun had reached its meridian that
Kanousky entered the town, a stranger not indeed to all, for
he knew Joseph's friends. But he doubted whether they
would receive him. They might possibly be of the same spirit
as Joseph was; yet he thought he would venture. The
children had been kind to him, and so indeed was their father.
He prayed for direction. He went, determining to tell the
whole truth. With a trembling hand he knocked at the door.
The children saw him approaching the house, and rushed to
open the door to Kanousky. He was welcomed in, and soon
many questions were put to him. Where was Joseph? Why
did he not come too? How was his master?

Kanousky replied to them, and told their father his
situation, and what had happened. He thanked the children,
too, for having taught him to read, and for many little
kindnesses he had received from them. At the same time,
everything he said was accompanied with so much
seriousness and simplicity, and was so unattended by any ill
will or censures, either to his late master or any of his old
companions, that though the father of the children, who was a
man that respected religion, yet, not a spiritual man, did not
implicitly believe all that Kanousky stated to him, neither did
he disbelieve it. He told Kanousky he might remain at his
house for the present, and in the meantime he would obtain
employment for him.

And here for a time did the Indian Christian continue; and, by his obliging conduct and great diligence, soon gained the good-will of his host; so that it was not very long before he was able to recommend him to a friend who wanted a servant. This friend had repeatedly observed Kanousky's attention and seeming devotion to the chapel; and he was induced, from what he had seen, and from the account he heard of the reasons which obliged him to quit his old master's service, to engage him on a little farm which adjoined the town. Here Kanousky grew in the esteem of his new master, for in all he did as a servant, he fulfilled that precept, "Be diligent in business."

In this farm, to his great joy, Kanousky found the servant upon whom the care of it devolved to be a man that, in a scriptural sense feared God, and who attended the chapel in which he had heard things "new and strange."

With this servant, whose name was James Irving, Kanousky loved to be whenever his employment allowed him; for whatsoever this man did, he sought to do "all to the glory of God," and thus adorned the religion of Christ in the eyes of our young Indian.

James Irving lived in the little farm-house, with his family, which consisted of his wife and two daughters. James and his wife were drawing near to forty years of age when Kanousky entered under their roof; his eldest daughter was twelve years of age, and his youngest not more than nine. Every morning, a small portion of that time which was allowed for breakfast was spent in prayer and thanksgiving to the "Father of mercies." I say a part of that time, because he said that "he had no right to use his master's time for family prayer, since then he would be robbing his master to serve God, and that with such service God would not be well pleased." In the evening, after all labour had ceased, a portion of the Bible was read, and sometimes a few remarks made upon the passage; a hymn sung, and prayer and praise offered to our condescending God who, though He "dwelleth

23

in the heavens, and filleth all things with Himself," loves to be addressed by His people with sincerity and reverence.

On the sabbath this family went twice to a place of worship, accompanied by Kanousky. The two little girls were exceedingly fond of the Indian and he was always kind to them. Every day he felt more happy in his new situation; and after he had been there some time, and had gained the confidence of the family, his heart overflowed with joy and thankfulness on account of his removal from his former master.

After a time Kanousky was baptised, and further, he received that token of the Redeemer's dying love to His people, the Lord's Supper. As he approached to participate in the great privilege of being a guest at that blessed feast, he seemed absorbed in new reflections upon the love of Christ, which passeth knowledge. When he ate the bread and drank the wine, tears flowed from his eyes; but they were tears of humility, penitence, joy and thanksgiving. He received a blessing, "for the Holy Spirit witnessed with his spirit" that he was a child of God.

Kanousky returned home silent, but deeply thoughtful; and his thoughts, as he afterwards declared, were these: "Me happy; me want nothing, me have all me desire in this world; me live here as long as God like, and then me ready, me like to die. Yes, me want one thing, me want a more thankful heart, me want never to sin."

The writer of this little memoir might add much respecting the conversation which took place in the evening between Kanousky and James Irving, but it would swell these pages to too great an extent.

In the evening, before he retired to rest, as usual he spent some minutes in prayer to God; but if he had ever prayed with more heart than usual, that evening was the time. His heart was like a spring from whence came an overflowing stream, for the words proceeded from his heart; there they arose, and indeed that only is acceptable prayer which issues from the heart.

CHAPTER EIGHT

A Visit to the Old Master

"Pray for them which despitefully use you,
and persecute you."
—Matthew 5:44

"How poor the life, if earthly store
Be all the riches one can show;
For jewels, gold, possessions rare,
Can ne'er to us true wealth bestow."

For several years Kanousky had been living at the farm, in James Irving's family. He had heard very little of his old master and of his former fellow-servants. But as those who are deeply concerned about their own salvation feel for the spiritual wants of others, he had for some time in secret grieved over the mode of life which his late master and the servants led. He began to make inquiry after them, and as he heard it was about the time of year when Joseph came to the town, he determined if possible to see him.

He obtained permission to have a holiday, and on that day he called upon the friend who first took him in after he had been turned out of his former master's service. Here he found Joseph, who was very glad to see him; nor was Joseph a little astonished to find Kanousky grown tall and dressed so well, and also to hear him speak so very sensibly on most points. There was something too in Kanousky's manner, so obliging and even polite, that Joseph sometimes doubted whether he was the same Kanousky whom he had known formerly. The Indian had learned from one whom he called "dear good Paul," that courtesy was a Christian's duty.

"And how," said Kanousky, "are my good master, and all my good friends, my old fellow-servants?"

25

"Surely," thought Joseph, "this is strange: master and all of us turned him out of house and home, and yet he does not remember the injury, but calls us all good."

"Master," rejoined Joseph, "is very ill; he has a severe fever, and it is very doubtful whether he will recover."

'Oh, I am very sorry," replied the Indian, for he now talked very well, and no longer used the word ME for I; "how I should like to go and see him."

"Well, if you can get permission, I return in two days, and I shall be truly glad of your accompanying me, provided you are not afraid of the fever."

"I am not afraid, and I will ask leave of my master."

Kanousky then inquired after all the servants by name, and was informed that the fever had, a few days before, carried off one of them from time into eternity. He dropped a tear and prayed silently that God would in mercy, for the sake of Jesus Christ, sanctify the trouble with which it had pleased Him to afflict his old master's family, to the good of the whole household.

In the evening when he returned home, he laid his wishes before James Irving, without consulting whom he scarcely did one single thing. James highly approved of Kanousky's desire to see his old master, and failed not at family prayer to seek for God's blessing upon his visit, should he go. Permission was readily granted for Kanousky to accompany Joseph, and his master allowed him, if he chose, to extend his stay so long as a month.

When the time arrived, Kanousky took an affectionate adieu of James and the family, after having been commended to the care of Almighty God, and set out for the town where Joseph was. But our Indian returned to his old master's house, not as he left it, for we remember then he travelled on foot, whereas now he had the use of one of his master's horses.

It was late at night when Joseph and Kanousky arrived at the end of their journey. The family had retired to rest, and they, not wishing to disturb the house, laid themselves down to rest upon some loose straw in a barn. Kanousky was a long time, though wearied, before he fell asleep; his mind was so full of what had taken place in former years on this spot. And though, indeed, he had saved some money, yet it did not amount to more than a hundred dollars. Still he could not help inwardly exclaiming, when he looked at his decent and respectable dress, as he arose in the morning, "'Godliness hath the promise of this life, as well as of that which is to come.' Since I have served God, how abundantly hath He provided for me!"

When the servants had risen they were all surprised to see Kanousky, and most of them were much pleased to meet him again, though others, when they perceived how respectable an appearance he bore, secretly envied him. But his frankness and kindness, and the affection with which he took their hands, soon dissipated every unpleasant feeling which any of them might entertain towards him.

Joseph was not long before he informed his master of his meeting Kanousky, and of Kanousky expressing a wish to visit him, and that he had brought Kanousky with him.

"You have!" replied his master; "how good, how kind of him, poor fellow; let him, if he is not afraid of the fever, come up and see me." Kanousky was soon introduced to the sick chamber. As he approached it, he prayed that God would prosper his visit for good to his late master: and the nearer he drew to the room, the more fervently did he pray.

When he had entered, he most respectfully bowed, and said, "I am very sorry, my dear master, to see you so ill, and I hope you will excuse the liberty I take in coming to see you."

His master, as he lay upon the bed, knew the voice and features of his old servant immediately, though years had made some alteration; but the words which that young man had just uttered went to his very heart. He was silent, a tear stole down his cheek; he considered that he did not merit this kindness; for he had certainly, to say the least of it, been unkind to Kanousky in turning him out of his house for no fault whatever.

"Right glad I am to see you, my good lad," said the farmer, "and it is very kind—indeed it is, of you to come so far to see me. Give me your hand, Kanousky," continued he, as he held his forth; "but no, my lad, you shall not touch it, perhaps you may receive the infection."

"Oh, my dear master, I am not afraid of the fever; allow me to take your hand." So saying, he took his hand, and pressed it between each of his own.

"You see me very weak, brought low indeed, but I am hoping to get better soon."

"I hope so, too," said Kanousky.

As Kanousky looked upon his old master, he felt compassion for his lost state of soul, and was longing to be a means of directing him to serious thoughts about eternity. In this state of doubt he lifted up his heart to God, to endue him with wisdom and courage. While he was thus musing, the farmer said to him—

Kanousky, you look sad; you seem thoughtful; is anything the matter?"

"Oh, master!" answered the Indian, "I think you seem very ill, and I hope God will spare your life some time longer."

"What!" exclaimed the farmer, "do you think me in danger?"

"I do not wish to frighten you by what I have said, master, but—" Here he paused.

"But what?—speak freely, my lad," said the farmer.

"But I think if you get a little worse, you would die; and then I think, where would your soul go?"

"To heaven, I hope."

"So I hope, master; but heaven is a prepared place for a prepared people, and if we are not prepared by God's Holy Spirit, through the merits of Jesus Christ, we cannot go to heaven."

"Well, my lad," returned the farmer, "I am too poorly to talk much at present; you must come again in the evening and see me."

Thus this man did as thousands do on a bed of sickness; for so soon as a Christian begins to converse upon matters connected with eternity, then they find themselves too ill or too much fatigued to hear what might be said. Indeed the heart, by nature, does not like these things, or else people would not avoid conversing upon death and judgment.

As Kanousky left him, he still hoped, as he had broken silence upon his master's danger, and upon the necessity of having repentance toward God and faith in our Lord Jesus Christ, that he should be able to resume the conversation at another opportunity.

When the evening came, Kanousky hastened to pay his master a second visit; but, alas! the poor patient was light-headed. His mind wandered from one subject to another, and he scarcely knew his nurse. The next day he was a little better, but too weak to see any one, or even to speak beyond a whisper.

What was to be lamented very much was, that the nurse was taken ill with the same complaint, which seemed now to be sinking the sick farmer into the bottomless pit. Though she was only slightly attacked, yet such was the panic throughout the house, that though she found every assistance from her young daughter, each one seemed afraid to wait upon the master. While the servants were all in a state of alarm, and each waited for the other to step forward, Kanousky offered his services, which were gladly accepted by the rest.

Nor was he deficient in his attention to his master; he was by him night and day, barely having repose to support nature. Under his diligence, it pleased God to raise up the farmer, who became filled with admiration at Kanousky's tender regard towards him, and whose esteem for the young Indian equalled that admiration. When the farmer inquired of Kanousky how it was that he chose to risk his life as he had done, Kanousky answered, "I placed my life and do commit it every day into the hands of my God; and I know, whether I live or die, I am safe."

The impressions made upon the farmer's mind were never afterwards removed.

But soon Kanousky was taken ill, and though he had a severe attack, yet he was restored, under the Divine blessing. And do not be surprised to hear that the man who had befriended him in the early part of this history became his nurse, and declared before all the house that he "would not mind suffering in attending to such a Christian as Kanousky." Throughout his illness he showed to all who saw him that a real Christian need not be afraid of "the terror by night, nor for the arrow that flieth by day, nor for the pestilence that walked in darkness, nor for the destruction that wasteth at noon-day." He proved to them, too, that "to him to live was Christ, and to die is gain."

Kanousky's illness had detained him longer at the farmer's than he at first intended to remain. A messenger, however, had been dispatched to his master, to inform him of his illness. At length he thought himself sufficiently recovered to return home. When he announced his intention, the farmer was grieved to think of being deprived of him, and would have willingly retained him in his service, but he knew that he must "not covet his neighbour's servant." He bade Kanousky visit him as often as convenient, and also to send him, from the town, several Bibles and tracts as soon as possible.

CHAPTER NINE

The Startling Discovery

"God moves in a mysterious way
His wonders to perform;
He plants His footsteps in the sea,
And rides upon the storm."

The morning came when Kanousky was to set out, and a most affectionate parting took place between not only himself and his master, but also between him and some of the servants; others, indeed, were glad when he went away, for they hoped their master would not, as they said, continue a saint.

He got safe back to James Irving's by the evening, who with his wife gave him a most welcome reception. Over the supper-table Kanousky gave them an account of what had taken place at his old master's, for which they afterwards, on their knees, and with overflowing hearts, thanked Him that delighteth to show mercy.

About three months after this, a lady of fortune who had business at the town came thither. She was acquainted with Kanousky's minister, and in the course of conversation, learned the history of the lad. This lady, with her servant, a female, partook of the Lord's Supper the following Sunday. After the service was concluded, she accompanied the minister to his house. That good pastor sometimes invited Kanousky to take a little refreshment in his kitchen with an old servant, who was the very man that originally invited Kanousky to enter into that "large house, where much noise was made."

While the lady was in the parlour with the minister and his family, they heard a loud shriek issue from the

31

kitchen. It was most grievous, so much so, that master, mistress, and visitors, all ran down stairs. When they had come into the kitchen, they found the lady's servant fallen on the ground in a swoon, Kanousky standing with his hands clasped, and, looking up toward heaven, tears streaming down his face, exclaiming, "Blessed God! Blessed God!" The old man was assisting the poor woman to rise.

"What's the matter, what's the matter?" said the minister, while his wife got some water to bathe the temples of the lady's servant. The old man for a moment or two seemed to be struck dumb, but presently uttered, "he has found his mother, and she has found her son." The poor woman revived, but she fainted again. At length she was relieved by a flood of tears, and then she called out, "My son, my son!" as she embraced him; and he exclaimed, "My mother, my mother!"

When the parties from the parlour found her calm, they retired, beckoning the old man to walk away with them. As soon as they had all come into the parlour, the minister said, 'Let them indulge their affection uninterrupted, and do, John, tell me what has passed."

John began and spoke as follows: "You know, master, I have always loved Kanousky as though he were my own child; and he, I think, has never failed to love me, and to tell me all his heart. This evening, finding that the lady's servant seemed to love God, he talked much of the love of God to his soul, and in the course of conversation, he said he never could thank God enough —no, not through all eternity—for bringing him, an Indian boy, to know the true God and Jesus Christ whom He hath sent. When he had said the words, 'An Indian boy,' the woman exclaimed, 'Are you an Indian?' Kanousky replied, 'Yes, I am nothing better.' 'Tell me your history,' said the woman anxiously, 'I will,' said Kanousky; but oh, sir,' he only uttered a few sentences before the woman gave that shriek and then fell upon Kanousky's neck, crying out, 'My son!' and afterwards fell on the ground where you saw her; and I believe he is her son."

Parents, do you read this account? Children, do you read these pages? Then I need not describe to you the happy scene that took place between Sazia and her son. That evening they praised and blessed God for His mercy and goodness; and the minister and his household did likewise.

* * *

Here the narrative abruptly ends. Doubtless the reader is left wondering what the after history of the now so happily reunited mother and son might be. Of one thing we can be confident: if it pleases the Lord to begin the good work in a poor sinner's soul, He will perform it until the day of Jesus Christ, and heaven's convoy, goodness and mercy, will attend that favoured sinner all the days of his life, and he will dwell in the house of the Lord for ever.

"When life's tempestuous storms are o'er,
How calm he meets the friendly shore,
Who lived averse to sin!
Such peace the Christian's path attends
That where the sinner's pleasure ends,
The good man's joys begin."

DAVID BRAINERD,
THE INDIAN'S MISSIONARY

The best of all stories are those that are true. Many of the wonderful tales of warriors and heroes are only fictitious tales of men who never lived, save in the imagination of the writers. But the story I am about to tell you is the true life-story of a man who went forth, constrained by love, to brave the dangers and bear the trials of a true soldier of the cross. It is not a highly-coloured tale of fiction, but a story of fact, which shows what God can do for and by a true servant of His, far away from home and friends, in a land of war and blood. It shows how one constrained by the love of Christ left home, kindred, and all that earth holds dear; and how, amid tribes of Indian braves, he spoke about the true God and Jesus Christ and His love, which wins the heart and changes the lives of all who are born again and who by faith receive it. I hope you will listen to me with patience while I try to tell it to you.

The hero of my story lived at a time when there were no railways, with their fast trains rushing through continents, or fast steamers ploughing the seas. Those who traveled had to do so on horseback or on foot, and those who went out to distant lands had to cross the stormy seas in small uncomfortable vessels, such as are only used for coasting coal ships now. And there were no large cities, with their broad streets, majestic buildings, and electric lights in those days. Where the great commercial cities of America, with their thousands of inhabitants now stand, there was nothing but wild prairie, with its long waving grass, through which herds of buffaloes and other wild animals ranged, chased by the Indian on his swift warhorse. Here and there a tribe of feather-plumed warriors had their camp, and sat around their wigwams smoking the pipe of peace, when not at deadly war with their fellows. I hope you will try to remember this while I tell my story.

Chapter One

The Orphan Boy of Hartford

Among the persecuted Puritans—as those who clung to the Word of God and who proclaimed the gospel of Christ in its simplicity were in those days called—was a good and earnest preacher of the name of Peter Hobart. He was obliged to flee from the little village of Hingham, in the county of Norfolk, where for many years he had served the Lord, and crossed the seas to New England, where the men of the Mayflower had preceded him. There he gathered a number of people around him and formed a village, to which he gave the name of his former home in Norfolk. For two generations we lose sight of this little colony, but in the third, we find the grandchildren following in the footsteps of their God-fearing parents.

At the beginning of the 18th century, in the town of Hartford, in Connecticut, a family of the name of Brainerd lived, who, on the mother's side, were the great-grand-children of the good man Hobart.

In this family was a weak and sickly boy named David, who, before he was twelve years old, was an orphan, his father having died when he was nine years old, and his mother some time after. So little David Brainerd was left in the care of strangers. At the time of his mother's death, the weakly boy was very anxious about his salvation, and so lonely was he, with no one to comfort him or point him to the Saviour, that he often wished himself dead and with his mother in heaven. But then the thought would cross his mind that he was not ready, for he had not been converted to God, and he knew that apart from this, he could not enter that holy, happy place. The dear lad, having no one to tell his trouble to, or to ask counsel from, set himself to earn salvation by his own works. He was working at this time as a farm labourer, and after his hard day's work was over, he gave his evenings to study, being anxious to improve the scant education he had got. For a year or more, David continued to work on the farm, and during that time he had made considerable progress in educating himself—so much so, that he was advised by his grandfather's successor at Hartford to "study for the ministry" and to withdraw from the company of other young men, so that he might give himself fully to the study of holy things. Whatever may be thought of such advice, given to a yet unconverted young man, it was over-ruled in the providence of God to bring him out from the company of many frivolous youths with whom he had been in the habit of spending some of his time, and of giving him new companions of a better kind. A few of these young men met every Sunday evening in a private room to read the Bible and to help each other to a knowledge of its teaching; and, in the mercy of God, young Brainerd was led into this little circle just at the time when his mind was deeply exercised as to the matter of his personal salvation.

One of the exercises of this Bible Students' Class—as we may justly name it—was to commit large portions of the Word of God to memory and to repeat them aloud at their gatherings. In order to be able to do his part in this healthy exercise, Brainerd was frequently heard repeating his "portion" aloud when alone in his little room at the midnight hour. But you must not think that this, important as it is, brought salvation to David Brainerd's soul. It cannot be earned or purchased by any sort of religious exercises. It must be received as the free gift of God's sovereign grace, through Jesus Christ alone, and the only qualification necessary to the possession of it is, to own one's self a sinner, and to flee to Christ, yea, to trust in the Lord Jesus as the only Saviour. But this David Brainerd did not know; so he struggled on, trying to make himself a Christian by works of his own. For weeks and months, he was in great distress, for the harder he struggled the further off did his salvation seem. He struggled like a drowning man, and wearied himself, but would not come to Jesus, Who is the only Saviour of sinners.

But we shall soon see a different picture; we shall see him happy in Christ. He says, "One morning, as I was walking as usual, in a solitary place, I saw at once that my contrivances to procure salvation for myself were all in vain; I was brought quite to a stand, finding myself totally lost. I now saw that it was forever impossible to save myself. I had the greatest certainty that my state was forever miserable for all that I could do, and was astonished that I had never seen it before. I now saw that all my prayers and fasting did not lay the least obligation upon God to give me His grace, that there was not the least good in them, because they were not performed from any love to God.

"I continued in this frame of mind from Friday morning until Sunday evening following, July 12, 1739. While I was walking in the same solitary place, unspeakable glory seemed to open to the view of my soul. It was not an outward brightness, or body of light; but it was a new inward view of God, such as I never saw before. I stood still and admired. I had never seen any thing before comparable to it for the excellency and beauty. It was very different from all the thoughts I had ever had of God or divine things. My soul rejoiced with joy unspeakable, to see such a glorious Divine Being; my soul was so captivated, and delighted with the excellency, loveliness, greatness, and other perfections of God, that at first I scarcely thought there was such a creature as myself. I continued in this frame for some length of time, without any sensible abatement. I felt myself in a new world, and everything appeared with a different aspect from what it used to. At this time the way of salvation opened to me with such wisdom, suitableness, and excellency, that I wondered I should ever think of any other way. I was amazed that I had not dropped my own contrivances, and complied with this blessed and excellent way before. If I could now be saved in any of the ways I had tried before, my whole soul would have refused. I wondered that the whole world did not see and comply with this way of salvation entirely by the righteousness of Christ."

It was something different than a dream or a vision which Brainerd received from heaven. Conversions that are affected by means of visions and dreams are not to be relied on, as most frequently they are the fruit of a disordered brain, or the work of Satan to dupe and deceive the soul. When one's personal and eternal salvation is at stake, something more substantial than a dream is required to give the assurance of it, and that something is the Word of God, which liveth and abideth for ever. When a sinner rests on Christ's finished work, and believes God's immutable Word, he has a foundation and an anchor which cannot be moved.

This was just what brought salvation, and the assurrance of it, to David Brainerd's soul that mid-summer Sunday evening, as he walked amid the woods. The Spirit of God, who had been convicting him of sin, had now shown him the beauty of Christ, and he, like the bitten Israelite in the desert, looked and lived. His joy was now full, and everything around seemed to be full of brightness. The old world was just the same, but a new life had been begun in Brainerd's soul. He had been born again, became a new creature in Christ, and this Christ was his Jesus by faith, his Redeemer. He felt much as one of our poets has written:

> Heaven wears a brighter blue,
> Earth a robe of sweeter green,
> All around a lovelier hue,
> By my former eyes unseen.
>
> Brighter suns around me wheel,
> Brighter stars above me shine,
> Everywhere I only feel
> I am Christ's and He is mine.
>
> Sin or death, or hell's alarms
> Cannot shake my hallowed rest,
> I am on my Saviour's arms,
> I am on my Saviour's breast.

Chapter Two

The Young Student

Yale College, in New Haven, has for long been famous as a seat of learning. It was there that David Brainerd went in 1739, a few months after his conversion, with many misgivings, for there was little to help a young man as David was in instructing and that he may grow in grace. This proved to be so in Yale, for, insofar as the "heads" of the College were able, they sought to hinder real spiritual work from being done. But God is a Sovereign, and in spite of men's opposition and wrath, He works.

A great revival began among the students at Yale, into which Brainerd threw himself with all his heart. His burning zeal for souls led him, perhaps, beyond the bounds of prudence at times; but so deeply in earnest was he in seeking the salvation of his fellows, that he deemed no sacrifice too great in order to reach them with the gospel. His efforts aroused the jealousy and indignation of his superiors, and they watched their opportunity to vent their anger on the young freshman. At the close of one of their meetings, a young man asked Brainerd's opinion of one of his tutors, a Mr. Whittesley, who had no favour for the converted students or their meetings. "He has no more grace than the chair I am leaning on," was Brainerd's unwise reply, which someone overheard and carried to the rector of the College. This supplied them with the opportunity they sought for to put an end to the students' meetings and to get rid of Brainerd, who was looked upon as the moving spirit of them. A counsel was held, and some who overheard the remark of Brainerd were called upon to give evidence against him. Trivial as the offence was, compared with many others which were daily allowed to pass unpunished, the judges brought in a verdict of "guilty" against Brainerd, and demanded that he should make a public confession of his guilt and humble himself before the College. This was doubtless intended to degrade the Christian student in the eyes of his fellows, that his influence over them might cease, and that he would be deprived of the honours to which he was justly entitled as the first prize-man in his class. This David politely refused to do, maintaining that however unwisely the words had been spoken, they were true, as had been too clearly shown by the life and conduct of the individual referred to; for it ought to be remembered that a place of distinction in a college or a church does not always imply a special endowment of God's grace, or in fact that the person thus honoured has been converted at all. This brought matters to an issue, and David was expelled from Yale.

It would be wrong to say he did not feel this humiliation, for though bold and fearless in his denunciation of sin, and in his adherence to what he believed to be of God, and according to truth, he possessed a very sensitive nature, which winced most keenly under the harsh and altogether unjust sentence pronounced against him. But there was no appeal, and so with feelings which any who have suffered for righteousness' sake, and because of speaking out what others may have whispered, will readily understand and sympathize with, Brainerd turned his back upon Yale once for all and went forth as a stranger in the world.

The next time we hear of him is in a very different sphere, but one spiritually more healthy. Far from the contests and scorn of college life, the young believer pursues his studies in the quiet village of Ripton under the roof of the Christian minister. There he had many hallowed seasons of communion with God, and it was no doubt there, in the "backside of the desert," alone with God, that he was "qualified" for that life of hardness and endurance to which God, unknown to him, was then leading his young servant. It has been God's way in His own school before sending them forth on their life-work. Moses was forty years in Horeb being educated by God in the backside of the desert for the great work of leading out from Egypt and leading on to

Canaan His people Israel. David on the plains of Bethlehem, keeping his father's flock and preparing to rule the kingdom, John the Baptist in the wilderness, Paul in Arabia, and, greater than all, Jesus at Nazareth for 30 years. before being sent forth to public service, show the Lord's way is the same with all His chosen servants. It was during these waiting hours that he became exercised about the condition of the heathen, and yielded himself to God, willing to go or to stay, as He might direct. This is the true spirit and the right place for the Lord's servant.

Chapter Three

Among the Indian Wigwams

Brainerd began to preach the gospel to the Indians in a place called Kent. He had little acquaintance with their language, yet the people came in crowds to hear him, and many were impressed and awakened to the reality of eternal things under his preaching. He did not keep back the truth, but spoke out plainly about sin and its punishment, as well as of a full and free salvation. This is the sort of preaching which the Spirit of God always uses to arouse and convert sinners. While thus engaged making known the gospel to the little colony of Indians there, his heart was much drawn out for the tribes in the north and west, who had not even heard the Saviour's Name, and he often prayed that God would open a door and send His messengers among them. These prayers were answered in a way he little expected.

A number of earnest Christian men in New York had heard of the godly young missionary, labouring among the Indians in that quiet corner. They sent him a message asking him to meet with them on a given day in New York, at which they told him of their desire that the gospel should be carried to those tribes of Indians living in heathen darkness, and laying before him the mission, as one to which in the providence of God he might be called. Brainerd was not the man to shrink from such an undertaking, however unworthy and unfit he might feel himself to be for it. At this crisis the young missionary had much private prayer and close dealing with God. The hour had come when the great choice of his life had to be made, either to go forth into the midst of these bloodthirsty savages—as many of them were—with the gospel, taking his life in his hand, or to turn from it to a sphere of fewer hardships and privations. As the call of God came with more and more clearness to his soul, he was enabled to count the cost, and to yield himself to God, for the work and the warfare to which he had been called, assured that he would not be sent on a warfare at his own charges, but upheld by the mighty hand which was beckoning him thither. In the beginning of the year 1743, at the age of twenty-five, and about four years after his conversion, David Brainerd bade farewell to the low friends he had upon earth, scarcely hoping ever to see their faces again; and disposing of his little property and effects, he rode away on his horse alone, without an attendant, into the wild wastes where the face of the white man had never been seen. After riding for many miles, he came upon an Indian settlement. The young missionary, weak, emaciated, and suffering from disease contracted through riding through swamps and forests, looked upon the wigwams, with their strange and weird-looking dwellers for whose salvation he had left all that earth could give.

The first effect of being consciously alone in the midst of the heathen was anything but pleasant, and Brainerd, while at certain times very happy and full of faith and fearless devotion, was at other times the victim of great darkness and depression. Riding along toward the Indian encampment he was very happy, but immediately on coming up to it, he was seized with a sense of deadness and darkness which caused him to turn aside and cry to God for support. The place that Brainerd had reached was named Kanaumeck, a densely wooded settlement mostly inhabited by Indians, near to Albany in New York. The only place of abode he could find was in a hut, with a heap of straw for his bed, belonging to a man who had lately come from the Highlands of Scotland to settle there, and who spoke Gaelic, of which Brainerd did not understand a word. Without a friend to converse with, or one to do him a kind act, his body worn out with long journeyings, his only food a little boiled corn, with heathen darkness everywhere around, we need not wonder that the dear man wrote in his diary the following words, which he never thought would go forth to the world a century after, to encourage and to cheer saints and servants of God passing through trials and difficulties: "I have no comfort of any kind, but what I have in God. I live in a most lonesome wilderness. I have no fellow-Christian to whom I might unbosom myself, or lay open my spiritual sorrows, with whom I might take sweet counsel and join in social prayer." Yet in the midst of all this, Brainerd clung to the living God, and often in his strange surroundings had happy seasons. His greatest trial was the occasional visits of white men, who taught the Indians many vices and brought strong drink among them, which greatly hindered the spread of the gospel. One aged chief said to Brainerd one day, "You white men bring us firewater which degrades our young braves, and diseases which kill our people; how can you expect us to believe in your religion?"

In order to free himself from all connection with such conduct on the part of the whites, he resolved to go and live wholly among the Indians, and make himself as one of them, but he would not allow himself to be chargeable to them. He provided for his own wants, often having to go long distances for bread, and frequently living days without it, at other times baking cakes of the coarse Indian meal, and thanking God for them as if he had been "in the circumstances of a king." He read and spoke to the Indians seated by the doors of their wig-wams, and was cheered by hearing several of them confess with the mouth the Lord Jesus, while their changed lives showed they were truly converted. But it was not to fall to the lot of Brainerd to reap; his work was that of a pioneer, and a breaker-up of the fallow ground. Others were to follow.

After seeing those who had been brought under the power of the Gospel handed over to the godly care of another, who had come to work amongst the Indians at the neighbouring town of Stockbridge, Brainerd again sallied forth with the hope of reaching the Indians on the forks of the Delaware, which he reached worn and wet, to begin afresh among a people to whom he was an entire stranger. He found the Indians of the Delaware very far sunk in every vice. They had idolatrous feasts and dances, with all their accompanying immoralities. This greatly distressed him, and he felt that he ought to testify against these scenes of revelry. But then, how could he? There he stood, a weak and solitary man in the midst of a warlike and uncivilized people. If he cried out against their sin they would doubtless turn upon him, and it might be to kill him. What was he to do? The whole night was spent with God in prayer, and when he went out from the secret tryst with the Most High the following morning, it was with a new energy filling his soul, so that he was able fearlessly to cry aloud and spare not. The result was that the dance ceased, the Indians quieted down, and in spite of the repeated attempts of their "medicine men" to get them away from Brainerd, they gathered around him and listened with rapt attention to the Word of God.

The religion of the Delaware Indians was a strange and crude idolatry. They reverenced and worshiped birds, beasts and reptiles, believing that they had power to do good to, or bring evil upon them, and in order to propitiate them and gain their favour they burned tobacco as incense to them. They had a kind of belief in a future state, but it was not gained from the Word of God, but by the divination and dreams of the Pow-waws or magicians, who had an immense power over them and were the most bitter opponents of the gospel. But the lone labourer, who had sown in tears, was about to reap with joy some of the fruit of his sowing; for the light of the gospel was breaking in upon the darkness, and the power of the Spirit of God—a Spirit altogether different from "the great Spirit" whom they acknowledged and worshipped after their heathen devices—was to put forth His gracious power and bring from among these red-skinned warriors of the wilderness a people to grace the Kingdom of the Son of God here upon earth, and by-and-by to join in the song of the redeemed in glory, around the throne.

Chapter Four

Remarkable Conversions

During one of his journeys, Brainerd heard of a small tribe of Indians living in a camp near Crossweeksung, in New Jersey. It was nearly a hundred miles from where he was, among the Delaware Indians; but this long distance through vast prairies, over rugged mountains and through trackless forests, sometimes on foot, sometimes on horseback, did not hinder the herald of the cross from reaching them. When he got to the place, exhausted after a long journey, he found they had nearly all left the place, only some three or four families being left.

This was by no means an unusual thing, for the Indians are a wandering race. Following the game across the prairie, or placing his wigwam in his frail bark canoe, he sails away with his entire family, it may be hundreds of miles, along the course of some mighty river, with its foaming rapids, or across some tranquil lake to a new abode. No wonder, therefore, that Brainerd found it difficult to follow up impressions made among these children of the wilderness.

The first congregation of Crossweeksung consisted of four women and a few little children—a small beginning, sure enough. But it is a remarkable fact that God's work often begins in a small and unpretentious way, whereas man makes a great flourish of trumpets with his. These four women told to their next neighbours, some miles away what Brainerd had told them about a God of love, and so deeply interested were they to hear the story for themselves, that when he next preached there were forty to fifty present, some of them from a distance of fifteen miles.

Among his congregation, he was glad to notice two or three who heard him preach at the Forks of Delaware, then with no apparent interest; now they listened most eagerly to the Word of God. And while the Word was spoken to that

46

eager circle of listeners seated around their wigwams in Crossweeksung, the Spirit of God came in great power with the truth, and many were deeply convicted of sin. It was a remarkable sight to see those ignorant men and women lamenting their sins, and crying for mercy, with tears gushing down their cheeks in floods. Then there was the joy of pointing them to the Lamb of God, and hearing from their lips the joyful confession that His precious blood had cleansed their sins away. He spent a joyful fortnight in that little settlement, the happiest and best he had known since he came to that waste wilderness with the tiding of the Redeemer's love.

The most remarkable case of conversion in this little revival was that of his interpreter, a man of about fifty years of age. This man was an Indian. He had been an habitual drunkard for many years, but upon entering Brainerd's service he became reformed, and prided himself on his "changed life." While Brainerd was preaching to a group of Indians one day, and this man interpreting his words, the interpreter became deeply awakened about the state of his soul, and cried out, "What must I do to be saved?" His prior reformation suddenly appeared to him as a garb of self-righteousness, and, as he afterwards said, he "saw that he had never done one good thing all his life." This was a grand discovery, one which every sinner must make before he will in conscious need cast himself on Jesus, the Saviour of sinners. This man was truly converted to God and was the first to be baptized by Brainerd "as a new creature in Christ Jesus." Others soon followed, and so wonderfully did the gospel triumph among those copper-coloured sons and daughters of the wilderness, that Brainerd was unable to leave them for long. He opened a school, which was attended by over thirty, and so diligent were they at their lessons, that in five months most of them were able to read the New Testament and there find strength and guidance as the children of God. To keep his "praying Indians" from the influence of the white men, where temptations and evil example did much to stumble these new-born souls, Brainerd removed them to Cranberry, some fifteen miles distant, and there in the seclusion of the wilderness, alone with God, he taught them His way more perfectly. It was a delightful sight as the setting sun threw his last beams across the prairie, to hear the voice of praise and prayer ascending from these assembled warriors of the wilderness, gathered with their wives and little children in peace around the man of God, who sat with the open Bible on his knee in their midst.

There every heart and voice is singing
Its praises to the Lord on high;
Far distant o'er the plains are ringing
The echoes of their heartfelt joy.

Praise we the Lord, for He has given
To us who sit in darkness, light
As yon bright sun lights up the heavens;
His Word has cleared away our night.

Chapter Five

An Abundant Harvest

Encouraged by the work of grace in Crossweeksung, Brainerd once again set forth along the banks of the Susquehannah, where he had sown so much of the precious seed, but which had hitherto borne no visible fruit in conversions. Ardently praying that God would begin to work among the Indians there, he rode into one of their camps, and before he could dismount from his horse a crowd of people gathered round, desiring him to preach to them. They were in great distress of soul, many weeping because of their sins. Brainerd's heart leaped with joy at the sight, and he immediately began to preach to them of the love of God. Later on the same day he preached again to them from the parable of "The Great Supper" (in Luke 14:16-23), setting forth the freeness and completeness of God's salvation to sinners, even the outcasts of the highways and hedges, such as they were. The effect of this preaching of God's free and boundless grace was very remarkable. Old men, little children, and even "medicine men" were melted into tears, and some of the "whites" who, hearing of the remarkable work of grace, came in a spirit of curiosity to see what was going on, were arrested; and others "who came to scoff, remained to pray." Such was the transformation wrought on these heathen men, who only a few weeks before had been idolaters, engaged in every form of folly and vice, and the sound thereof spread far and wide. One aged chief gave up his instruments of death, others brought their rattles and instruments used at the carousals and dances, where, in their unconverted days, they danced around an altar upon which the fat of deer had been offered in sacrifice, for hours yelling and swinging their bodies in all sorts of strange postures.

But all this progress was not allowed to remain unchallenged by the enemy. He incited the Pow-waws, or magicians, to oppose the work of God. They would come to Brainerd's preaching and utter their doleful sounds, chanting muttering incantations and using their charms for hours to prevent the people from hearing the gospel. Such is the devil's hatred to the glorious message. He dreads its power, for well he knows that if heard and believed either by the idolatrous Indians on the prairie, or by the refined and educated dweller in the city, it will set them free at once and for ever from his chain, and translate them into the kingdom of the Son of God. And that remarkable work of grace spread from tribe to tribe. Wherever the story of the redeeming love was told, sinners were converted. The Christian Indians came together at certain hours every day for prayer and the reading of God's Word, for they needed to be taught on everything. And Brainerd not only taught them publicly, but according to the apostolic pattern, "from house to house," or from wigwam to wigwam, until worn out with the long day's labour, he would lie down in his hut unable to do anything—tired in the work, but not tired of it; for the sweetest work on earth is to bring the blessed message of salvation to poor and lost sinners, and to guide the steps of new-born souls along the early stages of the heavenly road.

> Poor and afflicted, Lord, are Thine,
> Among the great unfit to shine;
> But, though the world may think it strange,
> They would not with the world exchange.

BRAINERD PREACHING TO THE INDIANS.

Chapter Six

Going Home in Triumph

While the work of grace was thus going on among the Indians, the worker was wasting away. The privations he had endured, and the continual strain from years of hard work, had broken down his constitution and brought upon him an incurable disease, which he knew must soon end his days of labour and carry him to the grave. Yet Brainerd, with unflagging zeal, laboured on. Often after a long day's work in preaching and visiting from wigwam to wigwam, with the glad tidings of a Saviour's love, he would lie down in woods and sleep there all night, awaking in a cold sweat. Then off again to another camp to preach the whole day. Many remarkable cases of conversion occurred during these busy days. When the Spirit of God used the word spoken to the awakening of the Indians to concern about their spiritual condition, some extraordinary scenes were witnessed. Crying out in agony of soul, powerful men lay on the ground, praying for mercy, and when they were brought to know the way of salvation, life, and peace through faith in the Lord Jesus, their joy knew no bounds. For although ignorant of the doctrines of the Word, they had received the Christ of God as their one and only Saviour, and when He comes into the heart He brings with Him joy and peace.

One aged Indian squaw, telling the story of her conversion in her own characteristic style, said: "When the Word was preached, it came like a needle to my heart, and I had no rest, day or night." The discourse of some of her neighbors who had been converted aggravated her distress. While in this awakened state she dreamed that two roads lay before her, one broad, another narrow. She tried to enter by a short gate leading into the narrow path, but some unseen power seemed to grasp her and hold her back. In this state she awoke and hastened to tell Brainerd of her distress, and what she had dreamed. The servant of God turned the dream to good account, by shewing the aged woman that she had been in the grasp of sin and Satan all her life, and that none but Christ could deliver her. After a time, her mind was enlightened to see God's way of salvation, and at the age of eighty, this Indian great-grandmother was truly converted and lived to bear a good testimony before three generations of her children to the saving power of the gospel of Christ. It was a great joy to Brainerd to see at last the good seed he had sown in tears, bringing forth its fruit, and to hear the songs of newborn souls in camps where nothing but dark idolatry had once held sway. But it was not to be his lot to reap the full harvest of his sowing. His strength was gradually ebbing away. When he could no longer go in and out amongst them, he preached from his couch to eager listeners, to whom his words seemed to come as from the very confines of eternity. In the Spring of 1747 he made a visit to the house of his friend Rev. Jonathan Edwards; who was of a kindred spirit, and whose preaching of the Word had been remarkably blessed—over five hundred, it is said, being converted under one sermon, on the words, "Their feet shall slide in due time."

There, under the roof of the man of God, in the company of earnest and devoted Christian friends, the evening of the worn-out servant was quietly spent, happy in the love of his God, waiting for the Lord to come and take him to eternal rest and joy.

September 17 was the last day that he went out of his lodging room. He was this day visited by his brother Israel. In the evening he was taken with a diarrhea, which he looked upon as another sign of approaching death, and said, "Oh, the glorious time is now coming! I have longed to serve God perfectly, now God will gratify those desires." He often used the word "glorious" when he spoke of the day of his death, calling it "that glorious day;" and the nearer death approached, the more he seemed to desire its arrival. He several times spoke of the different kinds of willingness to die; and spoke of it as a mean kind of willingness to die, to be willing to leave the body merely to get rid of pain.

In the last stages of his complaint, and confined to his room, he thus writes in his diary: "How infinitely sweet it is to love God and be all for him. While I was thinking thus, it was suggested to my mind, 'you are not an angel, lively and active;' to which my soul immediately replied, 'I do sincerely desire to love and glorify God as any angel in heaven.' Upon which it was suggested again, 'you are filthy and not fit for heaven.' Then appeared the blessed robes of Christ's righteousness, which I could but exult and triumph in. Oh, I knew I should be active as an angel in heaven, and stripped of filthy garments. But oh, to praise and love God more, and to please Him forever! This my soul panted after. Oh, that God might be glorified in all the earth! Lord, let Thy kingdom come! I saw that God had the residue of the Spirit; and my soul longed that it should be poured from on high. I could not but plead with God for my dear congregation, that He would preserve it, and not suffer His great name to lose its glory in that work."

His conversation at that time was heavenly; and he would break out in sweet expressions of love to God and desires for His glory. "My heaven," he said, "is to please God, and to glorify Him; to give all to Him, and be wholly devoted to His glory: that is the heaven I long for. It is no matter where I am stationed in heaven; whether I have a high or low seat there, but to love and glorify God, that is all. Had I a thousand souls, if they were worth anything, I would give them all to God: but I have nothing to give when all is done. It is a great comfort to think that I have done a little for God in the world; oh! it is but a very small matter; yet I have done a little; and I lament that I have done no more for Him."

With such expressions he mingled counsels to those around him; especially to the children. He told them in a plain manner what religion was, and its great importance, earnestly warning them to be satisfied with nothing but a thorough change of heart and a life devoted to God; and to not delay this great business. For he said to them, "I shall die here, and here I shall be buried; and here you will see my grave; and do you remember what I have said to you? When you see my grave, then remember what I have said to you when I was alive: then think how that man, who lies in that grave, counselled you, and warned you, to prepare for death. I am going into eternity, and it is sweet to me to think of eternity; but oh, what shall I say to the eternity of the wicked! I cannot think of it; the thought is too dreadful."

With perfect composure of mind, this servant of God saw the approaches of death and earnestly longed for the hour to come. Death to him was not an enemy, but a friend; it was the long expected messenger, sent to call him home to his heavenly Father's house, and he would exclaim, "Oh! why is the chariot so long in coming! Why tarry the wheels of His chariot! Come, Lord Jesus, come quickly." In this happy, expecting frame, he continued until October 9th, 1747, when his soul was received by his dear and beloved Lord and Saviour, and he entered into the full and perfect enjoyment of the heavenly city, the New Jerusalem. There he now lives in the presence of his God; and there, my young friends, we shall see him, if we love and serve the same God.

Thus lived, and laboured, and thus died David Brainerd, at the age of thirty years. How few, during a long life, have done so much to extend the kingdom of Christ. What joy will fill his soul forever, when he beholds the happy spirits around the throne of God, who were turned to Christ through his labours; while he joins with them in songs of praise and gratitude to God for His blessing, which made his efforts successful in their salvation. Oh! that the hearts of many, who read this account, may burn with a desire to go and do likewise; that many may catch his spirit, be the faithful disciples of Jesus on earth, and enjoy for ever and ever, the holy joys of those who turn many to righteousness: "They that turn many to righteousness, shall shine as the stars for ever and ever." Dan. 12:8.